ENERGY BOOST

Contents

Haydn Middleton

Story illustrated by
Dan Chernett

Heinemann

Find out about

- The food you should eat to keep fit and healthy

Tricky words

- fuel
- weight
- sweat
- exercising
- healthy
- competition
- weather
- healthier

Introduce these tricky words and help the reader when they come across them later!

Text starter

Does it matter what you eat and drink? Yes! Your body is like a car and the food you eat is your body's fuel. You need to eat the right fuel to get the energy you need to keep fit and healthy.

Body Fuel

Your body is like a car. You have to pump the right fuel inside it to make it work properly. The fuel you put in your car is petrol. The fuel you put in your body is food and drink.

Petrol can't make a car bigger and stronger, but the right food and drink *can* help you to grow!

What should you drink?

Did you know that more than half of your weight is made up of water?

When you are hot, some of this water comes out as sweat. The sweat dries and helps to cool your body down.

Then you need a drink to top up your body's fuel level.

Athletes can lose more than a litre of water an hour when they are exercising!

So what should you drink?

- **Water?** Yes!

- **Milk?** Yes!

- **Low-sugar fruit juice?** No problem.

- **Fizzy drinks?** Not so good if you drink too many of them. The acid and sugar they contain can harm your teeth and make you put on too much weight.

Where do you get your energy from?

Energy is the power to do lots of things without getting tired.

Your body can't create its own energy out of nothing. You need to feed your body with food and drink to get the energy you need.

Some foods are good fuel for your body.

- **Bread, rice, pasta and potatoes** give you energy.
- **Fruit and vegetables** keep you healthy.
- **Meat, fish and eggs** make you strong.
- **Milk, cheese and yoghurt** make your bones strong.

Crisps and sweets give you energy, but don't eat too many of them!

Eating a healthy diet

If you eat only one sort of food you won't have enough energy and you can even feel ill.

You also won't get all the vitamins and minerals that your body needs.

The best body fuel is a mix of all the different sorts of food. That will give you lots of energy.

Sports men and women are like sports cars.
They need high-energy fuel.
When they are training they eat lots of
meat, fish and eggs to give them strength.
Just before a race or a competition they eat
lots of pasta, rice and bread. These foods are
easy to digest and give them instant energy.
This mix of fuel means they can run
super fast!

Fat as a good fuel

Fat can be very useful to your body.

- It helps keep you warm in cold weather.
- It helps keep your skin and hair healthy.
- It can give you energy.

So your body does need fat in your body fuel mix. But where can you get this fat from?

Fat is in most of the foods we eat every day, like milk, cheese, butter and eggs. So it isn't hard to get enough fat in your diet.

But some kinds of fat are better than others. The fat in olive oil, nuts, eggs and fish is healthier for you than the fat in cakes, crisps and fried foods.

Fat as a bad fuel

Some foods, like chips and crisps, have too much of the wrong kind of fat in them. It's OK to eat these foods sometimes, but if you eat them too often you might:

- suffer from heart problems later in life
- put on too much weight
- have low energy levels because your fuel mix is not healthy.

Energy from healthy breads, cereals and pasta lasts longer than energy from 'fatty' foods.

How can you make sure you get the right amount of fat for your body fuel?

- Choose low-fat milk, cheese and yoghurt.
- Don't eat too much 'fast food'.
- Only have sweets and cakes sometimes.

So are you putting the right fuel into your body?

- Do you drink water or milk?
- Do you eat fruit and vegetables?
- Do you eat energy foods like bread?
- Do you eat strength foods like fish?

If you do, your body will have the right fuel mix and you will be healthy.

Quiz

Text Detective

- Why shouldn't you drink too many fizzy drinks?
- What is your favourite food? Is it good for you?

Word Detective

- **Phonic Focus:** Identifying phonemes in complex words
  Page 12: What is the long vowel phoneme in 'weight'?
  Which letters make the long vowel phoneme?
- Page 7: Find two smaller words in the word 'vegetables'.
- Page 8: Find two plural words.

Super Speller

Read these words:

lose   nothing   tired

Now try to spell them!

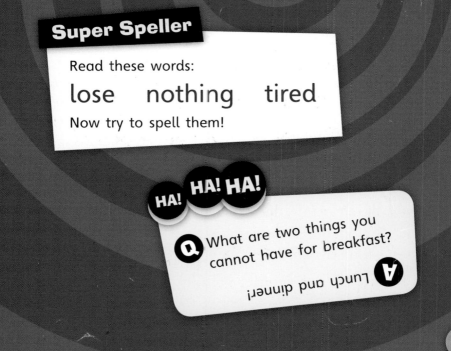

HA! HA! HA!

Q What are two things you cannot have for breakfast?

A Lunch and dinner!

15

 # Before Reading

In this story

Josh

Josh's mum

Chef Jeff

Tricky words

- training
- thirsty
- audience
- dreams
- microphones
- prefer
- yoghurt
- healthy

Introduce these tricky words and help the reader when they come across them later!

Story starter

Josh likes running and he is pretty good at it. But he doesn't do much training because he spends too much of his time watching TV. One day he was watching *Ready Steady Snack*, a programme where Chef Jeff shows people healthy food to eat between meals.

Ready Steady Snack

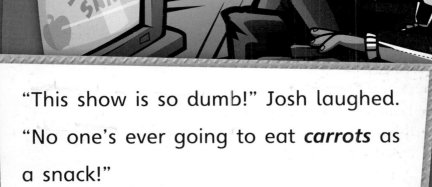

"This show is so dumb!" Josh laughed.
"No one's ever going to eat **carrots** as
a snack!"

"I thought you had running training,"
said his mum.

"Will you make me some chips first?"
asked Josh.

"No," said his mum.

Josh went into the kitchen. He was hungry. What could he have to eat? He picked up a bag of crisps and a fizzy drink, because crisps always made him thirsty.

Josh sat down in front of the TV with his snack. He blinked. The TV seemed to be coming closer. He blinked again.

No, Josh was getting closer to the TV.

He was being sucked towards the screen!

"Mum!" he called, "help ..."

But it was too late – he was sucked right inside the TV.

Josh found himself sitting in the front row of the audience in a TV studio. The audience was watching *Ready Steady Snack*. Josh still had his snack in his hands!

CAM2

STEADY SNACK

"So," Chef Jeff was saying, "if you fancy a snack between meals, chop up some carrots."

"In your dreams!" Josh said quietly. But the microphones picked up what Josh said. It was heard all around the studio.

What do you think will happen now?

Chef Jeff turned to look at Josh.

"Come up here!" he growled.

"Who, me?" Josh asked.

"Yes, you!" Chef Jeff nodded. "And leave that junk food by your seat!"

Slowly Josh got out of his seat and joined Chef Jeff in his studio kitchen.

"So you don't like carrots?" asked Chef Jeff.

"I prefer crisps," said Josh.

"You prefer crisps to carrots!" yelled Chef Jeff.

"Yes," said Josh. "And anyway, I can't cook carrots."

"The carrots are *raw!*" Chef Jeff shouted, and the audience laughed at Josh.

"Can you open a fridge?" Chef Jeff asked.

Josh nodded.

"Open that fridge then," said Chef Jeff. "Take something out."

Josh looked in the fridge. Right at the front was some low-fat yoghurt.

Josh picked up the low-fat yoghurt and turned to Chef Jeff.

"You're wearing a sports kit," Chef Jeff said. "What are you – a footballer?"

"No," said Josh. "I run. We've got a big race at school next month."

Chef Jeff frowned. "So you're getting ready for this race by filling up with crisps and fizzy drinks?"

"I was only having a snack before going to training," said Josh.

"But your body needs proper fuel to run fast," said Chef Jeff. "Too many fizzy drinks and crisps will slow you down! You need *healthy* snacks."

"But yoghurt doesn't taste good,"
said Josh.

"Then make it sweeter!" said Chef Jeff,
handing Josh a jar of honey. "Honey
is much healthier than the sugar in
fizzy drinks."

Josh mixed the honey into the yoghurt.

"*That* will taste yummy," said Chef Jeff.

Josh was not so sure.

"Now look in the freezer," said Chef Jeff.

Josh took out a plate of frozen grapes
on little sticks.

"I put the grapes in the freezer two hours
ago," said Chef Jeff. "They should be
just right now."

Chef Jeff picked up a grape on a stick, dipped it in the yoghurt and honey, and then popped it in his mouth.

"That is **so** good!" he said. "It's easy to make and you can use any sort of fruit. No cooking! Try one yourself."

Does this snack sound good to you?

But before Josh could reach for a grape … *ZAP!* It all went dark.

Josh found himself back on his sofa.

His mum had turned off the TV.

"Time for running training!" she said.

"I must have dreamed it," Josh thought.

But then he saw a blob on his knee.

It was yoghurt mixed with honey!

Chef Jeff was right. It did taste good.

Josh went into the kitchen and looked in the fridge. There was some yoghurt. There were no grapes, but there were strawberries and Chef Jeff had said any fruit would do. Then Josh checked in the cupboard. He saw some honey.

"YESSS!" thought Josh as he left for training. "I know what to have for my snack tomorrow."

Quiz

- Why was Chef Jeff cross with Josh?
- What healthy snack would you like to eat?

Word Detective

- **Phonic Focus:** Identifying phonemes in complex words
  Page 31: What is the long vowel phoneme in 'fruit'?
  What letters make the long vowel phoneme?
- Page 21: Find four plural words.
- Page 22: Find four different types of punctuation.

Super Speller

Read these words:

reach   yourself   easy

Now try to spell them!

HA! HA! HA!

Q Why did the chef get arrested?

A He beat up an egg!